FRENCH DAYS & TERMS OF THE WEEK
with PIWI ~ (The Posh Kiwi)

I have exciting news for you readers: I'm having a 'French Week'.

It's where I spend a week in France and indulge in only the FINEST French activities that Posh-Kiwi-Privilege can offer...

LUNDI (Monday)

I don't know what's more impressive~ the Eiffel Tower or the queue...

MARDI (Tuesday)

Simply beautiful. Leonardo DaFinchey really captured her hooter.

MERCREDI (Wednesday)

France has some of the best beaches on offer!

JEUDI (Thursday)

Crumbs! I forgot you need arms for this!

VENDREDI (Friday)

Only the FINEST foods with the FINEST wines for the FINEST of feathered fellows.

SAMEDI (Saturday)

LE VINEYARD

I enjoyed that wine so much last night, I want to see where it all came from.

DIMANCHE (Sunday)

Sitting down in a romantic café in Paris with someone I care about very much.

1) Lundi 2) Mardi 3) Mercredi 4) Jeudi 5) Vendredi 6) Samedi 7) Dimanche

There is just one snag about these 'Foreign Country Weeks'...

The following week never seems to be quite as enjoyable.

"aujourd'hui"

TODAY I received the bills for all my holiday expenses.

Including the bill for a slight indulgence in hotel room services YESTERDAY.
gulp

"hier"

GOLD JELLY

"demain"

I've got to buy more washing-up materials TOMORROW, with the last of my money...

"cette Semaine"

MANAGER

Because THIS WEEK I'm going to be doing nothing but wash dishes to pay off my debts.

"La semaine dernière"

And since LAST WEEK had some unfortunate incidents...

Get a move on!

Even better!

"La semaine prochaine"

Once I'm finished working off my bills, I'm to be forced out of the country NEXT WEEK

CURATOR

REPRESENTATIVE OF FRANCE

I hope you now know the French days and terms of the week.

Next time I'll be teaching you about debt.

1) Today   2) Yesterday   3) Tomorrow   4) This Week   5) Last Week   6) Next Week

SPELLING SPELLS
with WILMA
THE RULES OF SPELLING
and Wurton

Company Baby Difficulty
Ah yes, these will work.

ZING!

What are you up to, Wilma?

I'm magically making *words* with this new spellbook I found.

Rules of Spelling Spells

See, these words all have **consonants** before the 'y' But with a "*Spelling-Rule Spell*", I can change them into *different words*.

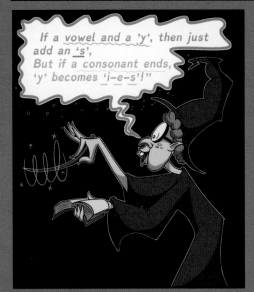

If a vowel and a 'y', then just add an 's', But if a consonant ends, 'y' becomes 'i-e-s'!

COMPANIES *BLOOP*

BABIES *BLOOP*

DIFFICULTIES *BLOOP*

With Wilma's spell, the 'y's become 'ies'...

Aren't I skilled? Bet you wish you could do that, Wurton.

BOP

Pah! Easy magic. *Wurton* will show you a Spelling-Spell that's *actually* useful!

SWIPE!

RULES OF ZLING SPELLS

What's he going to do? Spell his name...?

Now let's see... ah yes, I know *this* one.

Sens hoped ima ...icing exciting

If it ends with a *vowel*, or an "ing", "ed" or "ation"...

Ptchoo!

TOSS

Ptchoo!

...Lose the *silent 'e'* for this word-spell creation.

Lasers shoot from his wand

When you're ready, try out your magic on the **FULL** version of the spells, here.

IN FULL

(xceptions)

eight

beige

The 'i' before 'e', except after 'c',
but **NOT** when a _**"sh" sound**_ is found in the 'c'.

And **NOT** when the '_ie_' is _sounding_ like '_**A**_',
like it does so in '_neighbour_' and does so in '_weigh_'.

leisure

ancient

Did I ever tell you about the time I was a little girl on the Homefront during World War 2?

Yes, mum, several times! Why not talk about—

"Homefront", you see, is when vast numbers of civilians work together to support the war effort during a conflict.

I was part of the Homefront during the time of the 'Munich Crisis' in World War 2.

Civilians had to enrol in Air Raid Precautions (ARP). We lived in fear of attacks from the air.

SQUOOSH!

SQUEAL!

FORT LAWRA

Believe me, mum, I think we live in such fears today with Laura around.

ARP is still necessary.

LATER THAT DAY...

Speaking of air attacks, it was the Blitz that really tested us as civilians.

Oh is that right, Granny?

(Not Listening)

After the RAF won the 'Battle of Britain' in 1940, the German airforce began their attempt to bomb us into surrender.

Throughout 1943 and 1944, we suffered their terrifying V1 bombs...

...and V2 Rockets were also fired at us from mainland Europe.

GASP!

SPLAT!

SINUSES UNDER SIEGE

DAN'S BODY BATTLES

Not looking forward to this...

Watchoo! This cold has lasted a while! Why won't it just go away?

Meanwhile, Dan's immune system fights an ongoing war with the invading cold virus...

DAN'S ANTIBODY SOLDIERS

Darn-tootin' right, Private! Looks like our Dan's got a problem with his **sinuses**.

AMMO

That's 'cus it's not just a *cold* anymore, right, Sarge?

Uhm... Permission to ask what sinuses are, sir?

Why you're **FIGHTING** inside them *right now*, son!

They're air-filled pockets within the bone of Dan's head and face.

MUCUS
S.N.O.T.
(Some Nasty Old Trash)

Like the nose, sinuses have a thin, moist layer of tissue that creates sticky mucus - trapping things like dust and invading enemies.

Sinuses

MUCUS MEMBRANE

CILIA

Little hairs called 'cilia' beat back and forth to clear the mucus from the nose, to the stomach where it's burned by acids.

Gee-gosh, Sarge. That's quite a system. But... what do sinuses do?

YANK!

KABOOM!

Well, some say they keep the head from being too heavy ~ being pockets of air instead of bone.

They also give a person their depth and tone of voice. Don't you notice how strange Dan's gets when he's stuffy from a cold?

I owe my sleepless nights to it, sir...

CLICK!

MISS!

DODGE!

But what happens to sinuses when the virus just won't go away?

Good question, Private. A *cold virus* can...

Damage the *cilia* so that mucus is not swept away...

DROOP!

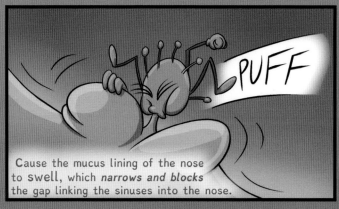

PUFF

Cause the mucus lining of the nose to swell, which *narrows and blocks* the gap linking the sinuses into the nose.

Lead to the production of more mucus, which is often *thicker and stickier*.

MUCUS GENERATOR

SPLUTTER

This makes it harder to flow out of the sinuses.

If all this chaos blocks the openings that usually *drain* the sinuses, then mucus gets trapped in them.
Like water in a stagnant pond, this makes a good home for fungi, viruses, and **bacteria**!

Fungus

Bacteria   Virus

BIG-BAD BACTERIA

If a cold lasts for more that 10-14 days, it may be a case of acute SINUSITUS ~ an infection of the sinuses.

ZIG!

If it were to last for 3 months, it could mean **chronic sinusitus**...

Fever...

Lots of 'nasal discharge'. (*Runny nose, sneezing, etc*)

SNOT BUCKET

PPTT!

Coughing (*especially bad at night*), with puffy eyes (*usually in the morning*).

Bad Breath...

I feel sick, mum.

So do I!

Cripes, Sarge! Too many bacteria have been created! What might this do to the body?

One of the things a <u>doctor</u> might do is check the pressure of the sinuses, *by tapping or pressing on your forehead and cheeks*,

Dr.Doc

If bacteria are causing the problems, the doctor may prescribe an antibiotic...

DROP!

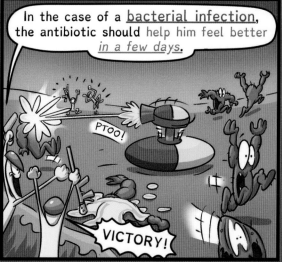

In the case of a <u>bacterial infection</u>, the antibiotic should help him feel better *in a few days*.

PTOO!

VICTORY!

FIGURES
OF SPEECH

Mr METAPHOR

He *listens* to you with a *wooden face*.
He *speaks* to you with *cotton candy words*.
An *ear-piercing scream* is *music to his ears*.

Ms Simile

She leaps off the ground *as if* it were a hot stove.
She is as light *as* a feather in the breeze, and
has a memory *like* a goldfish (with amnesia).

Ms Alliteration

She *C*an *C*reate a *C*ool *C*lone of a *C*at,
*b*ecause she is *b*lessed with a *b*rilliant *b*rain.

Mr Onomatopoeia

His mouth tends to *belch* as his nose gives a *honk*.
If he sees you his eyes give a cash register's *ca-ching*!

Mr Personification

Money is the *only friend* he has.
He sings *lonely songs* to the moonlight
as his candle-flame *dances* slowly in the dark.

Ms Hyperbole

She *never* stops working.
She drinks milkshake from a *bottomless glass*, yet
she's skinny enough to *jump through a key-hole*.

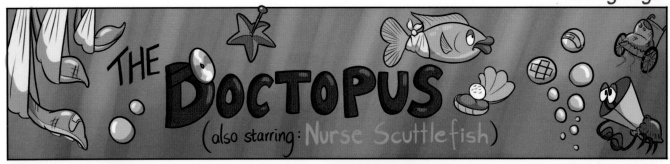

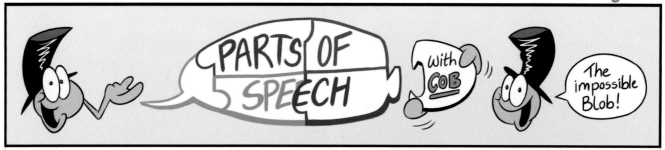

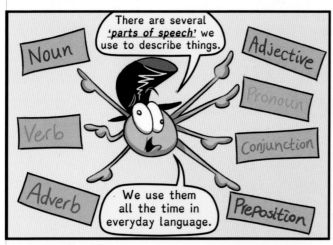

A NOUN is a word that refers to a person, place, thing, or event.

An ADJECTIVE is a word that describes a noun.

A VERB is a word describing an action.

Now, a **CONJUNCTION** is used to *link* words _OR_ parts of sentences together.

Rich **BUT** not happy

click

She went home _OR_ her mum was calling

He made it **SO** he could eat it.

There's so many conjunction words you can use: 'because', 'until', 'however', and more...

But here's an easy way to remember ones called 'coordinating conjunctions':

FOR
AND
NOR
BUT
OR
YET
SO

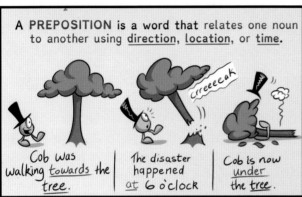

A **PREPOSITION** is a word that relates one noun to another using <u>direction</u>, <u>location</u>, or <u>time</u>.

creeeeak

Cob was walking <u>towards</u> the <u>tree</u>.

The disaster happened <u>at</u> 6 o'clock

Cob is now <u>under</u> the <u>tree</u>.

They usually consist of words like:

"BEFORE"   "AFTER"   BOOF! "BETWEEN"

"TOWARDS"   "AWAY"   "AROUND"

RAVINE   SNAP!

"BESIDE"   "OVER"   "IN"

Now <u>PRONOUNS</u> are interesting. They *replace* Nouns, usually when describing <u>people</u>.

Her

PRONOUN   Jenny   **NOUN**

I'll take over for a second.

Cheers, mate.

Pronouns are things like "he", "she", "they", "it". Once a noun has been introduced, they take over.

"<u>She</u> loved skipping"

"Jimmy hurt <u>his</u> knee."

"The phone was new, but <u>it</u> was out of battery."

First midges, now THIS!

Bzzz!

"Bees are dangerous when <u>they</u> swarm."

If a pronoun is like a team-mate for a noun, an **ADVERB** is one for verbs.

I'm *jumping*!

VERB

ADVERB

So *gracefully*...!

If a verb describes an action, an *adverb* describes **HOW** the action is:

The rocket <u>flew *speedily*</u> to the stars

WHOOSH!

The sun <u>shone</u> *brightly*

The dinosaur <u>roared</u> *furiously*

But they also work for *adjectives* too, as well as *other adverbs*.

"it was *incredibly* bright"

"*intensely* blazing."

I'm going to *<u>think</u>* *carefully* about what

interesting <u>words</u> I can use, <u>so that</u> I can

<u>make</u> <u>them</u> <u>into</u> *interesting* <u>sentences</u>.

See if <u>*you*</u> can come up with anything interesting using these **PARTS OF SPEECH**.

DEKKO FAN PAGE

Em, if anyone has any *future* questions about where to send unwanted sacks of gold, i'll give you my address. *(I also accept second-hand ones too ~ not fussy, here)*

YOUR Questions and Comments:

"I would definitely do my work this way."
(Anya Cowan - age 9)

"I need one for Higher Chemistry, now!"
(Sean Reilly – age 16)

"Do you make Modern History-based comics?"
(Lisa Pool - teacher)

DEKKO: *Indeed we do! We'll be making more in the future as the comics progress.*

Welcome to the *Dekko Fan Page!* Send us in your jokes, your art, your questions and more to our email: info@dekkocomics.com. You might see it pop up in the next Dekko you read...

I must say, Isla, you've got a talent!

Send in a Limerick

There once was a boy from Bearsden,
Who liked to dress up as a hen,
He once went to school
And looked like a fool
And never went back there again!

~ sent in by Laurie Slavin, Bearsden

Cob the impossible Blob
by Isla – age 9.
Excellent!

(I don't recall this photo being taken...)

What's Your Favourite Animal?

Eilidh Traynor says:
LEOPARD

Timbot & Crowball
by David – age 10.
Nice one, Dave!

Leopards are big predatory cats found throughout Africa and Asia.

They often bring their prey up into trees with them to keep it safe.

ASK EARNIE:

Q: What is the meaning of life?
(from Hannah McShane, Torrance)

None of your business.

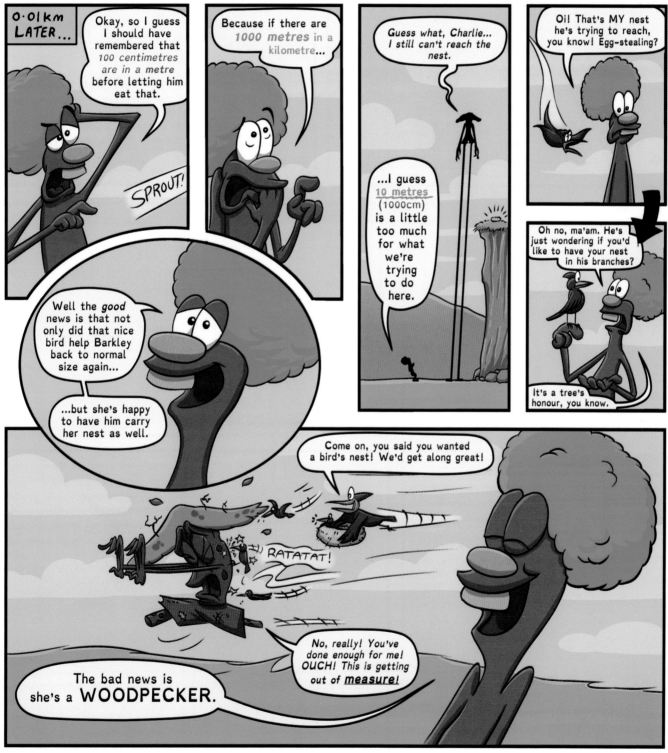

Well, I've had about 0.125 of the litre so far.

100ml would be 0.1 but 25ml extra is '0.025'.

Add them together =

0·125l

125 ml DRUNK

Simply move the 'point' to a different place and you've got a percentage.

BOOT!

12·5%

125 ml DRUNK

What's that in Fractions?

'1/8', of course. 125ml is an eighth of a litre.

Eight lots of 12.5% would be 100%.

Eight lots of 0.125 would be 1.

It's actually quite neat, when you think about it.

3 ways of explaining the amount of something.

Very useful, too!

For example, I can be happy in knowing that we have 87.5% of the cola left to drink AND half a pizza to eat too...

BURP!

Correction: we tragically have 0% of the cola and 0 pizza-slices left. Maybe 1/100 if you count the crusts.

DONG!

COLA

EMPTY

PABLO'S PIZZA

While I consider what to do to Earnie, read this comic over until you know it.

What's that in decimals?

THE END

PUZZLE

Find all six words:

B	J	O	B	N	L
X	A	A	M	O	U
G	H	B	T	U	N
V	E	N	I	N	D
H	I	E	R	E	I
O	V	I	R	U	S

- The French word for 'Monday'.
- The English word for *more than one baby*.
- The *part of speech* that refers to a person, place, thing or event.
- The French word for 'yesterday'.
- The name of the microscopic troublemakers who attack things like sinuses.
- The German word for 'yes'.

Colour the short and long hands so that they match the digital times provided.

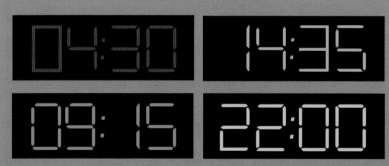

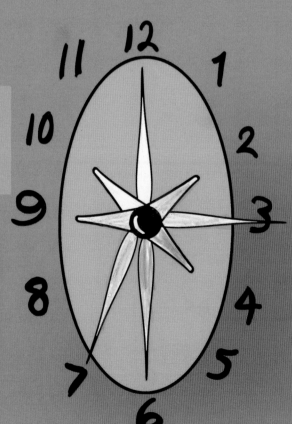

PAGE

This is my grand Great Grandfather, *'Bazillion the Great'*. See how many historical resources you can find in this photo. There's a bonus point for those who can see it...

Give the date of these events to reveal the year in which World War II began...

2	0	1	6	The year of the Rio Olympics.
	1	9	0 Ø	The year when food rationing came into force.
		4		The first year of the V1 Bombs and V2 Rockets attack on Britain.
		3		The very first year of the 20th century.

Answers are on the official website: www.dekkocomics.com

SPROCKET-FORCE

A force **is a** *push* **or** *pull* **upon an object as** the result of an interaction with another object.

Force of golf club *pushing* golf-ball.

Force of *hands* *pulling* golf club.

Whenever there is an interaction between two objects, there is a FORCE upon each object.

Force of the golf club *pushing* the ball

Force of the ball *pushing against* the golf club.

= the ball goes flying! (the result of the interaction)

When the interaction ceases, the two objects no longer experience force.

Club finishes swinging

Ball begins to fall

You think you're funny, don't you – Mr Artist.

Yep.

Force *only* exists as a result of *interaction*.

GLERK!

PLOP

Like the golf-ball and Sprocket's head, here.

POP

Anyway, all interactions between objects can be placed into TWO broad categories:

- Contact Forces
- Forces caused by Action-at-a-Distance

Biff

SUCK!

Contact Forces are types of forces caused by two objects physically touching each other.

Physical Contact

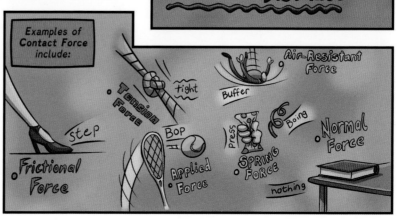

Examples of Contact Force include:

Step

Tension Force

Tight

Bop

Buffer

Air-Resistant Force

Press

Boing

Normal Force

Frictional Force

Applied Force

SPRING Force

nothing

Action-at-a-distance Forces are force interactions that result even when the two objects <u>are not touching</u> each other.

Use the force!

PUSH AWAY

PULL TOWARDS

They can still push and pull, even though they're separated.

1

GRAVITATIONAL FORCE

is one type. The sun and the planets have a *gravitational pull* on each other, despite the immense distance between them.

Sun

Earth

Earth

Moon

I'm gonna fly!

LAND

JUMP

Aw.

When you *jump*, the gravitational pull of our planet (Earth) drags you back down to the ground.

2

ELECTRIC FORCE

is the force that <u>exists between *charged particles*</u>. Electric Force is what makes your <u>hair stand</u> up on a cold day, and <u>lets you SEE</u> when a lamp is on in a dark room.

Shiver

Caused by **charged particles:**

3

Then there's # MAGNETIC FORCE.

You've seen how a magnet can <u>pull</u> metal objects towards it, right?

PULL

But have you ever put two magnets together? The *magnetic pull* they both have causes them to <u>push</u> away from each other. Very interesting...

PUSH

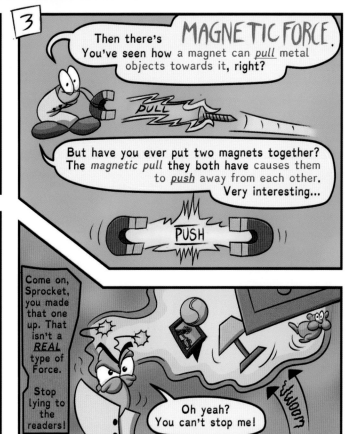

4... *wait, what?!*

And finally there's **TELEKINETIC FORCE**, where I can push and pull objects with the sheer *power* of my supernatural mind!

FLOAT

{WOOOMMM

Hershaw the Hamster

Come on, Sprocket, you made that one up. That isn't a <u>REAL</u> type of Force.

Stop lying to the readers!

Oh yeah? You can't stop me!

{woom

Very well, Sprocket. I won't **FORCE** you...

Rub Rub

You won't?

Nope. The <u>objects</u> will, though! Ha-Ha!

BOOF!

TALES of WORDS
THE KNIGHT AND THE DRAGON

Onomatopoeia: words that sound like what they mean.

Simile: descriptions involving 'like' or 'as'.

Metaphor: imagery WITHOUT the 'like' or 'as'.

Alliteration: two or more words beginning with the same letter or sound.

Irony: 'verbal' irony is when the opposite is happening in the context of what's being said.

Oxymoron: two opposite words put together to describe something.

Once there was a dragon, who lived in a Cool Comfy Cave Cooking chilli Con Carne.

And almost exactly every week he was rudely interrupted by an awful knight.

I shall slay thee, dragon!

You again?

The dragon, fed-up of being bothered like this, breathed fire on the big-headed buffoon.

Clear off!

PWOOFF!

But the knight's armour continued to *bling*, unharmed by the dragon's burning burp.

The knight was wearing special fire-proof armour, you see.

DRY CLEAN ONLY

Trying to roast it with fire was like trying to melt ice with snow.

DONK!

GROWL!

So there was nothing to stop the knight from walloping the poor dragon...

...and leaving him all beat-up; a heap of scales and stars, on the floor.

SNAP!

And then he would go and boast his story to the local village of '*The cool breeze of the dragon's breath*'.

DRAGON HILL

Everyone was impressed and called him '*The Fireproof Wonder*' ~ which sent the knight's ego through the roof!